Descant & Treble Recorder Duets *from the* Beginning

Teacher's Book

John Pitts

This collection of 22 easy mixed duets is suitable for two players or class ensembles, both accompanied and unaccompanied. It features a wide range of repertoire that varies from classical favourites to folk songs, spirituals, Latin American dances and 'blues', together with original pieces by John Pitts.

All the items are carefully graded, and the range of required notes increases steadily for both instruments, as indicated in the contents list in the Pupil's Book. But the desire to learn a particular piece will always provide the incentive to master any new note that stands in the way! Consolidation material is also included for each stage. At the start of the book it is expected that descant recorder players will have reached the beginning of *Recorder from the Beginning Book 2*, and treble recorder players will have learnt the first eight notes in *Treble Recorder from the Beginning*. Both these books are in the author's widely popular teaching scheme.

Within the 22 pieces, the musical interest is divided between descant and treble recorder, so that both instruments have equal opportunity to 'shine', often within the same piece.

The Pupil's Book includes guitar chord symbols, and some items also have suggestions for use of percussion instruments. The Teacher's Book includes piano accompaniments for all the pieces, as well as some additional pitched/unpitched percussion parts.

In keeping with the 'repertoire' nature of the book, only a minimum of teaching help or explanation is given. Where more help is required it is best to refer to the appropriate pages of the teaching scheme *Recorder from the Beginning.*

Chester Music Limited
(A division of Music Sales Limited)
8/9 Frith Street, London W1V 5TZ

Order No. CH61304 ISBN 0-7119-6682-6

Music processed by Stave Origination.
Cover photography by Patrick Harrison.
Cover design by Jon Forss.
Printed in the United Kingdom by Caligraving Limited, Thetford, Norfolk.

Contents

Chandos Fanfare Pitts

The recorder players will need to listen to each other carefully in this duet and count the rests. The descant begins, then the treble copies with some of the same music. When one part copies another we call it **imitation.**

Nobody Knows the Trouble I've Seen

American Spiritual

Spirituals are the religious folksongs of America. Negro spirituals arose among the black slave population of America. Many of them were versions of European songs and hymns, but with the Negro's own particular changes. For him the spiritual was not only a means of expressing feelings, but also a song of religious hope.

Many Negro spirituals only use the pentatonic (5 note) scale. This happens in 'Nobody Knows The Trouble I've Seen', so allows us to make up an accompaniment using ostinato patterns on the pentatonic scale. Here are some to play **instead of the piano/ guitar accompaniment.** You can use any two, three or all of them together!

Try to use a different pitched percussion instrument for each ostinato, e.g. soprano glockenspiel, alto metallophone and bass xylophone. A rhythm on tambourine will also help!

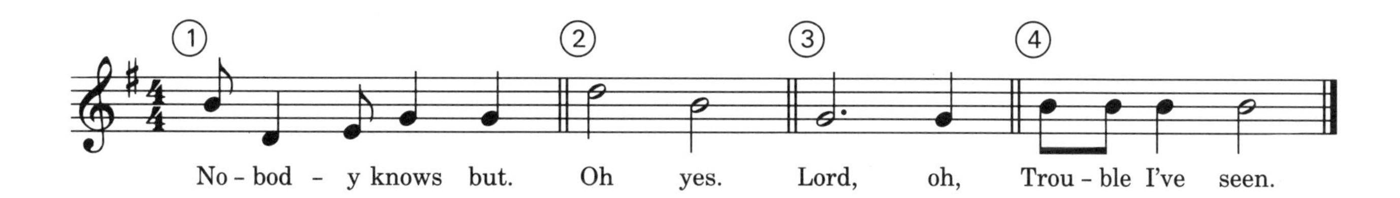

Zulu Lullaby   South African folk song

10
Dm
G7
C
C
Dm
Dm
G7
C
13
Dm
Dm7
G7
C
G
Am
16
Am
D7
G
Am
Am7
D7
G

19
G
C
Am
D7
G
C
22
Am
D7
G
G
Am
Am
D7
G
25
Am
Am7
D7
G
G
C

28
Am
D7
G
C
Am
D7
G
31
G
Am
Am
D7
G
Am
Am7
D7
G

La Mourisque Renaissance

13
D
G
D
G
F
G
C
Em
D7
1
G
18
2
& Fine
G
C
G
C
F
C
F
Dm
G
Fine
23
C
G
C
F
C
F
G
C
D7
D.C. al Fine
(without repeats)
D.C. al Fine
(without repeats)

Menuetto (from Divertimento KV213) Mozart

This Menuetto (Minuet) comes from Mozart's Divertimento in F Major KV213 for 2 oboes, 2 horns and 3 bassoons. It was written in 1775, when Mozart was working for the Archbishop of Salzburg, who had a grand palace, court and orchestra.

The Trio from the same Divertimento appears on page 34 in the Pupil's Book (Teacher's Book page 53).

A Divertimento was a lighthearted suite (collection) of several contrasted movements, meant to be easy to listen to — a 'diversion', in fact. They were often played either during meals, or in the garden for light entertainment. Apart from a good number of Divertimenti, Mozart wrote other similar light music called Serenades and Cassations.

Mozart (1756 - 91) is best known for his operas, symphonies, concertos, chamber music, church music and piano sonatas. He was a very busy composer and performer!

Swing Low, Sweet Chariot   American Spiritual

Some information about spirituals is given on page 7.

This is another spiritual that uses the pentatonic scale, so some suggestions are given below for three ostinato patterns. These can be used to make an accompaniment **instead of using the piano/ guitar accompaniment.** You can use any two or all three ostinati together.

Try to use a different pitched percussion instrument for each ostinato, e.g. soprano glockenspiel, alto metallophone and bass xylophone. A rhythm on tambourine will also help!

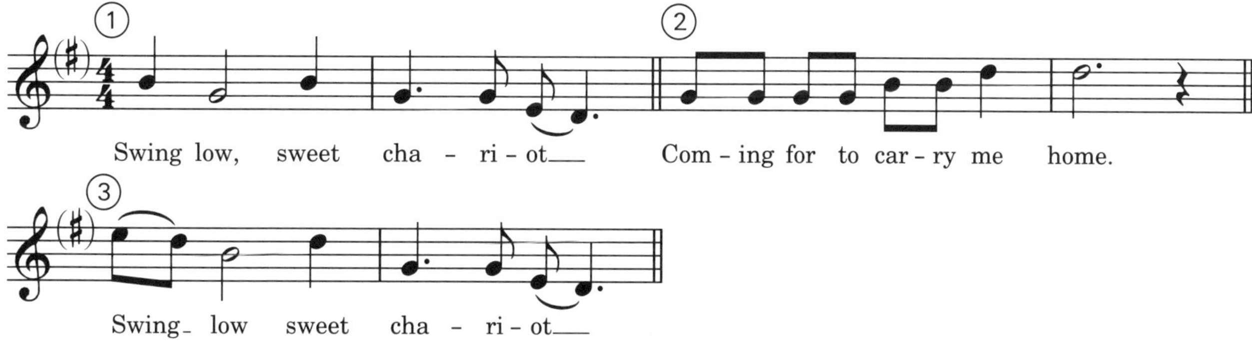

The Saints Traditional

13
Cm
G
D7
To continue
G
17
To Finish
G
C
G
Fine
(Guitar tacet)
C
Fine
21
C

25
A7
Dm
G7
C
29
C7
F
Fm
C
33
C
G7
C
D7
(Guitar tacet)
D.S. al Fine
D.S. al Fine

Guantanamera   Traditional Cuban tune

10
D7
G
C
D7
13
C
D7
G
C
16
D7
G
C
D7

The beguine rhythm accompaniment given on p.34 can also be used to enhance this piece.

Jefferson Blues   Pitts

10
C
G
13
D7
C7
G
D7
To continuo
To finish
16
G
G
Fine
Am
D7
Fine

19
G
22
G7
C
25
G
D7

The blues began about 1900 in the southern states of the USA. The main sources were the Negro work songs and spirituals that had been sung by the slaves, as well as the ragtime music which appeared in the late 19th century (eg Scott Joplin's 'Maple Leaf Rag' 1899).

Musically the strongest characteristic of the blues is its harmonic structure – the 'blues chord progression'. This is a 12 bar series of chords in a strict pattern:

line 1 – 4 bars on chord I
line 2 – 2 bars on chord IV, then 2 bars on chord I
line 3 – 1 bar on chord V, then 1 bar on chord IV, followed by 2 bars on chord I

A melodic characteristic of the blues is the use of 'blue notes' – flattened thirds and sevenths.

The first major composer of blues was W.C. Handy, a Negro cornet player and band leader who wrote 'Memphis Blues' in 1909 and 'St Louis Blues' in 1914.

Chaconne (from The Fairy Queen)
Purcell
Moderato (♩= 92)
Descant
Treble
G
D
Am
D
Em
G
6
C
Am
D
C
A7
D
G
D
11
Am
D
Em
G
C
Am
D7
G
D7
G
Fine
Fine

17
G
D
Am
Em
Bm
(✓)
Em
22
C
D7
Em
✓
A7
D
G
D
Am
✓
28
Em
G
(✓)
C
✓
Am
D7
G
D7
G
D.C. al Fine
✓
D.C. al Fine

Tango Chacabuco   Pitts

13
G
D7
G
Fine
Fine
8ve
17
C
G
D
G
21
C
G
A7
D
D.S. al Fine
D.S. al Fine

Soracaba Beguine Pitts

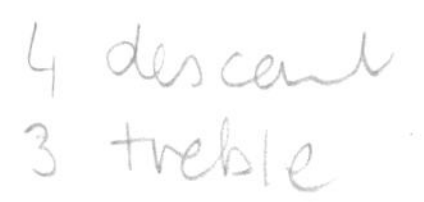

10
G
A7
D7
13
Bm
Em
C
16
D7
Bm
Em

The Pupil's Book includes the following suggestion for a rhythm ostinato accompaniment. This will enhance the piece, whether or not the piano is also used.

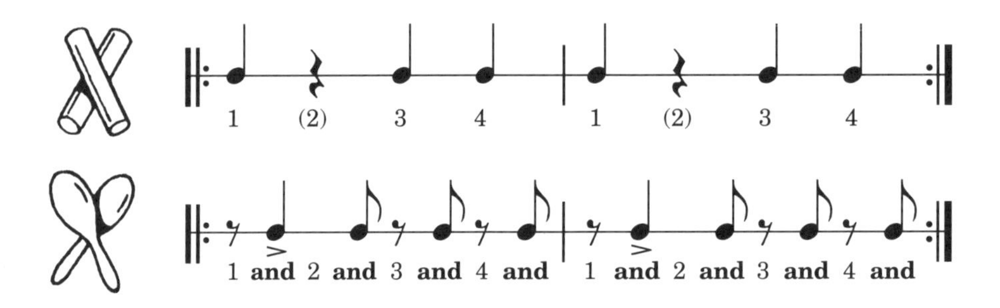

The same beguine rhythm accompaniment can be used for **Guantanamera** (page 21, Pupil's Book page 14).

Concert Waltz Pitts

16
D7
Bm
Em
21
C
Am
D7
Bm
26
G7
C
Cm
G
C/D
D7

To continue
To finish
31
G
D7
G
Fine
G
Am7
Fine
36
D
Am7
D7
G
C
42
Am
Bm
Em
A7
D
D.S. al Fine
D.S. al Fine

Cielito Lindo   Mexican

19
C
G7
C
F
25
Dm7
G7
C
31
G7
Dm7
G7
C

37
C
G7
C
F
Dm7
G7
43
C
G7
48
Dm7
G7
C

She Moved Thro' the Fair   Irish

13
G7
F
G
17
C
G
F
G
Fine
Fine
3
21
C
G
F
G

* The Pupil's part uses a D.C. instead of a D.S.

Helston Furry Dance Cornish Spring Festival dance

The Furry Dance at Helston in Cornwall is probably one of the oldest communal Spring Festival dances still surviving in Britain. It has been performed there for centuries, during which time the festival has been variously called Flora, Faddy, or Furry Day, the last being now the most usual name.

The dance is an ancient May ceremony which takes place on Furry Day, May 8th, which is also the Feast of St Michael, patron saint of the parish. Furry Day is still a tremendous occasion in Helston, with over 1000 dancers taking part during the day, and many thousands of spectators. The town is decorated with bunting, flowers and greenery. There are four dances during the day, at 7am, 10am, noon and 5pm.

Plaisir d'Amour Martini

12
Am
G
D7
G
Fine
Fine
17
G
C
G
C
21
G
D7
G

* Bar 33 onwards is written as a repeat in the Pupil's part, to avoid a page turn.

36
C
G
D
40
A
D7
G
44
Am
G
D7
G

Ragtime Pitts

13
F
Adim7
C
Am
D7
C
G7
C
17
C
F
C
F
C
G7
C
G7
21
C
F
C
D7
G7

Ragtime music developed in America in the 1890's as an early type of jazz. The piano style of the day had developed a bouncing, left hand bass and an elaborate, syncopated melody line. Because it sounded as ragged as a torn cloth it was called 'ragged time', then 'ragtime'. Its effect was catching and it spread rapidly from honky-tonk bars into theatres, dancehalls and via sheet music and piano rolls into homes throughout America.

Scott Joplin (1868-1917) was one of the first black composers of Ragtime piano music. His famous pieces include 'Maple Leaf Rag' and 'The Entertainer'. This recorder piece is written in the same ragtime style.

Trio (from Divertimento KV213) Mozart

The Menuetto by Mozart on page 14 is also from Divertimento in F major KV213.

25
D
A7
D
29
D7
G
33
G
C
G
C
G
D7
G
✓
✓
✓

Rondeau (from The Fairy Queen) Purcell

The Chaconne by Purcell on page 28 is also from the 'The Fairy Queen'.

Palmarito Rumba   Pitts

The **rumba** is a Cuban dance which uses a syncopated rhythm pattern. An important characteristic is the anticipation of second beat in the bass of each bar, resulting in this subdivision:

Claves can play this rhythm as an effective accompaniment.
An easier way to count it is as follows:

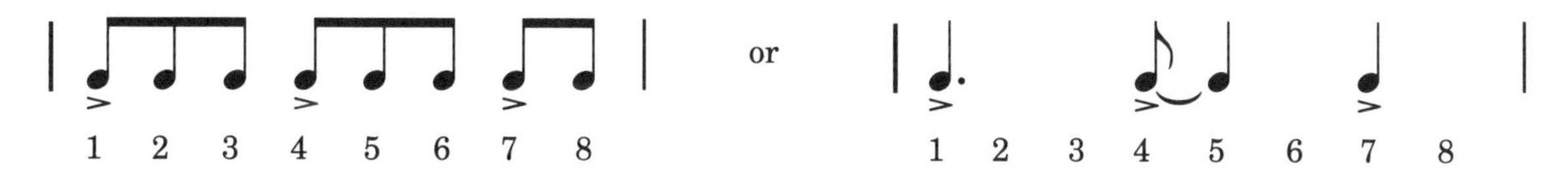

In addition to the basic rhythm of the bass line, accompaniment chords usually fill in all the quavers not played by the bass, as used in the piano accompaniment here.

Menuet (from Berenice)
Handel
Andante larghetto
Descant
Treble
G D C Bm Am A7 D D7 G D7 G
6
Am D D7 G Bm G Em
11
A7 D Bm A7 D A7 D A7 D

17
D C D7 G Am7 D C D7
22
G Am B Em Em C G C
27
D Am Em C Am G D7 G C D7 G

32
D G D C Bm Am A7 D D7
37
G D7 G D Em Am D7 G
41
G D7 G D7 Em Am D7
1
G
2
G

Recorder Duets *from the* Beginning

by John Pitts

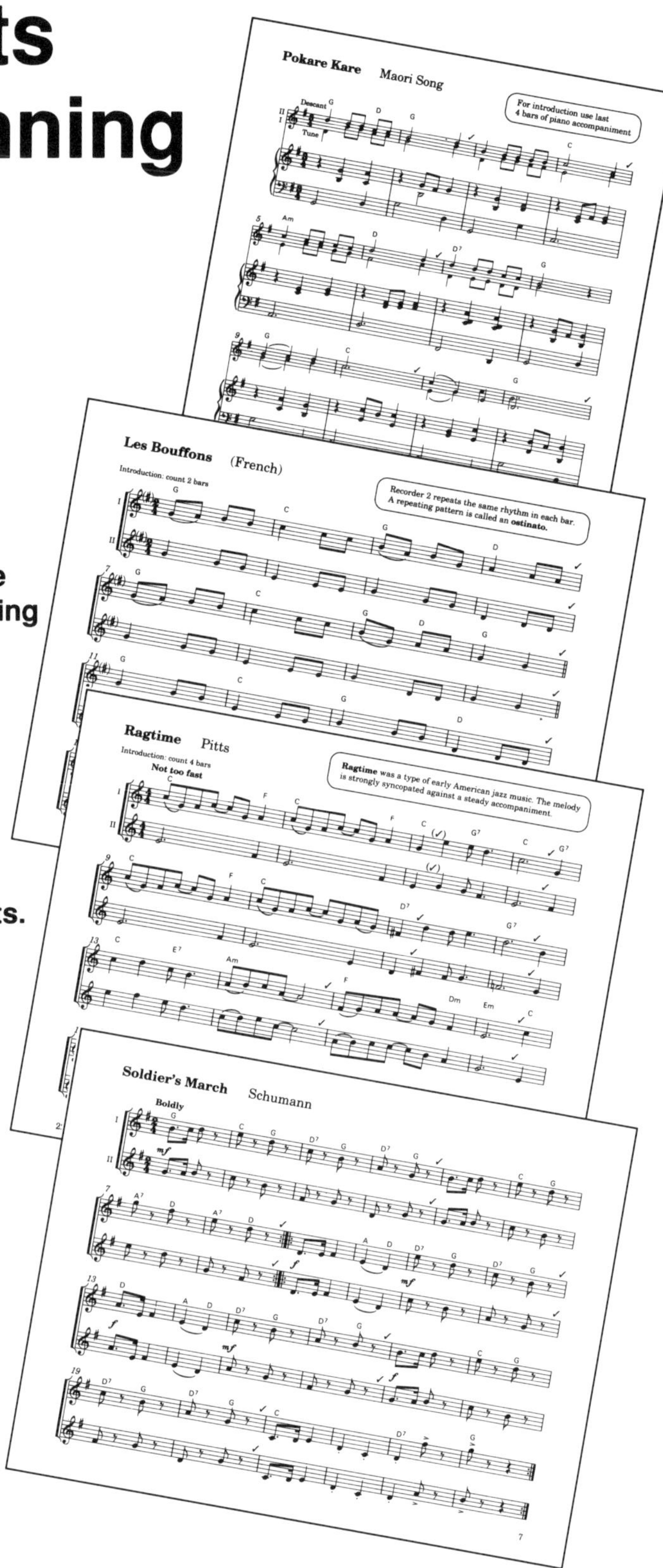

Three collections of easy duets for descant recorders, complementing the author's popular teaching scheme *Recorder from the Beginning.*

These superb arrangements, ranging from Beethoven to the Blues, bring all the benefits and enjoyment of ensemble playing and are suitable for 2 players or class ensembles.

Precisely graded by level of difficulty of notes included.

Guitar chords are included, along with piano accompaniments and suggestions for additional percussion accompaniments.

Book 1 CH61213
Book 2 CH61214
Book 3 CH61215

Teacher's Book 1 CH61251
Teacher's Book 2 CH61252
Teacher's Book 3 CH61253

Chester Music Limited
(A division of Music Sales Limited)
8/9 Frith Street, London W1V 5TZ